# LUDWIG VAN BEETHOVEN

# QUARTET

for 2 Violins, Viola and Violoncello
F major/F-Dur/Fa majeur
Op. 59/1
Edited by/Herausgegeben von
Wilhelm Altmann

T0080494

## Ernst Eulenburg Ltd

London · Mainz · Madrid · New York · Paris · Tokyo · Toronto · Zürich

# BEETHOVEN:
# STRING QUARTET F-MAJOR, OP. 59 No. 1

Following on the publication in 1801 of his string quartets op. 18, Beethoven completed in 1802 the quartet arrangement (in F-major) of his E-major piano sonata op. 14 No. 1, but several years elapsed before he again took up the composition of original string quartets. The chief incentive was provided by an order or request on the part of the art-loving Count Rasumovsky, at that time Russian Ambassador in Vienna.

The autograph of the first of these three quartets, since April 1909 in the possession of the Prussian State Library in Berlin, is inscribed by Beethoven: *Quartetto 1mo. La prima parte solamente una volta— Quartetto angefangen am 26 May 1806.—*

The composition of these quartets, which were at first not fully appreciated by his contemporaries, occupied Beethoven together with op. 56, 57, 58 and 60; they were completed by the end of 1806. In keeping with the custom of the times they remained unprinted for one year in the ownership of the Count who had ordered them and to whom they are dedicated. On the 18th November, 1806, Beethoven offered them in vain to Breitkopf & Härtel in Leipzig for publication at a fee of 600 florins. It is not quite certain which is the first edition. In the opinion of Dugge these quartets were published in 1808 under the title:

*Trois Quatuors pour deux Violons, Alto e Violoncello. Composés par Louis van Beethoven. Oeuvre 59me. Livraison 1, 2 and 3, respectively, a Vienne au Magazin de J. Riedl, 582. Hohenmarkt.* (Plate numbers 580, 584, 585.) Nottebohm, however, quotes as the publishers *"Vienne au Bureau des arts et d'industrie a Pesth chez Schreyvogel & Comp."* with the same plate numbers. Probably he is right. We know that the firm of Johann Riedl in Vienna, which closed down in 1829, took over these quartets from the Bureau which was bankrupt in 1811.

The third cover page of the Riedl edition (and probably that of the original) is decorated with the Rasumovsky crest, the motto of which reads: *"Famam extendere factis",* and underneath there is the following dedication:

*Trois Quatuors Tres humblement Dediés à son Excellence Monsieur le Comte De Rasoumoffsky Conseiller privé actuel de Sa Majesté L'Empereur De Toutes Les Russies. Senateur, Chevalier des ordres de Saint André, de Saint Alexandre-Newsky et Grand-Croix de celui de Saint Wladimir de la première Classe &c. &c. par Louis van Beethoven.*

In honour of Count Rasumovsky Beethoven embodied a Russian folk song both in the first and the second quartet.

The Russian theme used in the Finale of No. 1 is included as follows in the Collection of Russian Folk songs published by Iwan Pratsch, which was known to Beethoven (cp. G. Nottebohm, *Zweite Beethoviana,* 90):

The metronomic figures were added by Beethoven at a later date (1823).

## VARIOUS READINGS

Evident errors in writing on Beethoven's part are:

I. the notation of the viola in the 1st movement, bar 132 (score p. 6, syst. III, bar 4)

as given (in accordance with the autograph) in the original edition, by Heckel, Holle-Liszt, B. & H., and also by Joachim-Moser.

The reading given by Peters-David

is certainly preferable; the same applies to—

II. the repetition of the second theme in bar 280 (score 12, IV, 5). It is obvious that the 1st violin should play D flat, as correctly stated by Joachim-Moser, although the autograph clearly reads D.

III. In the Allegretto vivace, bar 56 (score 20, I, 5), the other better known score editions (with the exception of Holle-Liszt, and the old and the new Peters editions) give the 2nd violin.(in accordance with the autograph) as follows:

It appears that it should read:

IV. With regard to marks of expression bar 99 (score 21, II, 6) is worth mentioning. In Peters and B. & H. (score and parts of the latter) the *pp* mark is shown in all four parts under the first note. The Mannheim edition, *however* (probably the first reprint), and also Holle-Liszt, give the following reading:

The 1st violin has no mark, and in the other parts the *pp* is under the second note. The variant is explained by the fact that the autograph originally had the latter notation which was subsequently changed by Beethoven. The

# BEETHOVEN:
## STREICHQUARTETT F-DUR, OP. 59 No 1

Zwar hatte Beethoven im Jahre 1802 seinen 1801 erschienenen Streichquartetten op. 18 die Umarbeitung der E-dur-Klaviersonate op. 14 Nr. 1 in ein Quartett (in F-dur) folgen lassen, allein es vergingen mehrere Jahre, bis er wieder an die Komposition von Originalstreichquartetten ging. Die äußere Veranlassung dazu war ein Auftrag oder Wunsch des kunstliebenden Grafen Rasumovsky, des damaligen russischen Botschafters in Wien.

Das Autograph des ersten dieser drei Quartette, das seit April 1909 im Besitze der Königl. Bibliothek in Berlin ist, ist von Beethoven überschrieben: Quartetto 1mo La prima parte solamente una volta-Quartetto angefangen am 26. May 1806. —

Die Komposition dieser Quartette, die von den Zeitgenossen zuerst nicht recht gewürdigt worden sind, beschäftigte Beethoven neben seinen Werken 56, 57, 58 und auch 60; sie waren am Ende des Jahres 1806 vollendet. Der Sitte der Zeit nach blieben sie ein Jahr lang ungedruckt im Besitze des Auftraggebers, dem sie auch gewidmet wurden. Am 18. November 1806 bot sie Beethoven der Firma Breitkopf & Härtel in Leipzig für 600 Gulden vergeblich zum Verlag an. Jetzt ist ganz aufgeklärt, welches die Originalausgabe ist. Nach Herrn Dugges Ansicht sind diese Quartette im Januar 1808 er-

schienen, und zwar unter dem Titel: Trois Quatuors pour deux Violons, Alto e Violoncello. Composés par Louis van Beethoven. Oeuvre 59me, Livraison 1, bzw. 2, 3 a Vienne au Magazin de J. Riedl. 582. Hohenmarkt. (Stich-No 580, 584, 585.) Nottebohm aber gibt als Verlag „Vienne au Bureau des arts et d'industrie a Pesth chez Schreyvogel & Comp." mit den gleichen Verlagsnummern an. Er hat recht; wir wissen, daß die ca. 1829 erloschene Firma Johann Riedl in Wien diese Quartette von dem 1811 in Konkurs gegangenen Bureau übernommen hat.

Die dritte Umschlagseite dieser Riedlschen (und wohl auch der ursprünglichen) Ausgabe ist mit dem Wappen der Rasumovsky — der Wahlspruch lautet: Famam extendere factis — geschmückt, unter welchem folgende Widmung steht:

Trois Quatuors Tres humblement Dediés à son Excellence Monsieur le Comte De Rasoumoffsky Conseiller privé actuel de Sa Majesté L'Empereur De Toutes Les Russies. Senateur, Chevalier des ordres de Saint André, de Saint Alexandre-Newsky et Grand-Croix de celui de Saint Wladimir de la première Classe &c. &c. par Louis van Beethoven.

Dem Grafen Rasumovsky zu Ehren hat Beethoven in dem ersten und zweiten Quartett je ein russisches Volkslied eingeflochten. Das im Finale von No. 1 ver-

same applies to the parallel phrase (score 31, II, 7).

V. In bar 434 of the same movement (score 32, IV, 3) Heckel, Holle-Liszt, Peters-David, and B. & H. show the 1st violin thus –

in accordance with the autograph. Comparing this with the corresponding phrase in the violoncello (8 bars previous) we may assume an error in writing on Beethoven's part in the 1st violin. Hence Dugge's version, which has also been adopted by Joachim-Moser,

does not seem entirely unjustified.

VI. The D in the 1st violin in the final bar (score 33, IV, 11) which is shown in the newer editions (in agreement with the autograph) in a notation requiring it to be played on the G- and D-strings simultaneously ($\rho$), is just given as ($\downarrow$) in the Mannheim edition and by Holle-Liszt.

VII. Furthermore, the repetition of the shake notation at the beginning of the Thème Russe is remarkable in bar 134 (score 45, II-III) and in bar 233 (49, II-III). In the Heckel edition (as in the autograph) the chain of shakes is not interrupted but links the five minims without accentuating the first bar of the Allegro. But Peters (David and also Joachim-Moser) and B. & H. accentuate the entry by a repetition of the *tr* mark.

Wilh. Altmann

wendete russische Thema erscheint in der von Iwan Pratsch herausgegebenen Sammlung russischer Volkslieder, die | Beethoven gekannt hat (vgl. G. Nottebohm, Zweite Beethoviana 90), in folgender Gestalt:

*Molto andante*

Die Metronomierung ist später (1823) von Beethoven festgesetzt worden.

## Varianten

Als offenbarer Schreibfehler Beethovens dürfte

I. die Notierung der Viola im Satz I, Takt 132 (Part. pag. 6, Syst. III, Takt 4)

anzusehen sein, wie nach dem Autograph Orig.-Ausg., Heckel, Holle-Liszt, B. & H., auch Joachim-Moser angeben. Die Schreibweise bei Peters-David

ist entschieden vorzuziehen; dasselbe gilt

II. von der Wiederholung des zweiten Themas Takt 280 (Part. 12, IV, 5). Daß es hier in der Viol. I ♭ $\overline{d}$ heißen muß, wie auch Joachim-Moser richtig haben, ist zweifellos, trotzdem die Originalhandschrift deutlich *d* hat.

III. Im Allegretto vivace findet sich Takt 56 (Part. 20, I, 5) die Viol. II in den anderen bekannteren Partitur-Ausgaben (mit Ausnahme der Holle-Lisztschen, sowie der alten und neuen Petersschen) dem Autograph gemäß

notiert; es muß statt dessen doch wohl

heißen. Hinsichtlich der Vortragsbezeichnung ist

IV. Takt 99 (Part. 21, II, 6) erwähnenswert. Bei Peters und B. & H. (letztere Part.- und St.-Ausg. ist hier die *pp*-Bezeichnung in allen 4 Stimmen vermerkt, und zwar zu der ersten Note. Die Mannheimer Ausgabe (wohl ziemlich der erste Nachdruck), ebenso Holle-Liszt hat aber so:

also Viol. I, ohne Bezeichnung, die übrigen Stimmen aber *pp* erst zur zweiten Note. Die Verschiedenheit erklärt sich daraus, daß das Autograph ursprünglich letztere Bezeichnung

hatte, die aber Beethoven nachträglich geändert hat. Das gleiche gilt auch von der Parallelstelle (Part. 31, II, 7). V. findet sich Takt 434 eben dieses selben Satzes (Part. 32, IV, 3) die Viol. I bei Heckel, Holle-Liszt, Peters-David und B. & H. folgendermaßen getreu nach dem Autographen

notiert. Vergleicht man hiermit die korrespondierende Stelle im Violoncello (8 Takte vorher), so darf man wohl auf einen Schreibfehler. Beethovens in der Viol. I schließen; es dürfte demnach die auch von Joachim-Moser adoptierte Abänderung Dugges

nicht ganz ungerechtfertigt sein. VI. Das *d* der Viol. I im Schlußtakte (Part. 33, IV, II), welches dem Autograph gemäß in den neueren Ausgaben als auf der G- und D-Saite zu nehmen notiert steht (♩), ist in der Mannheimer und Holle-Lisztschen Ausgabe nur einfach (♩) geschrieben. — Auffällig ist ferner VII. die Wiederholung der Trillerbezeichnung zu Anfang des Thème russe Takt 134 (Part. 45, II—III) und Takt 233 (49, II—III). In der Heckelschen Ausgabe ist, wie im Autographen, die Trillerkette n i c h t unterbrochen, sondern bindet, o h n e M a r k i e r u n g d e s e r s t e n T a k t e s vom Allegro, die fünf halben Noten aneinander. Peters (David und auch Joachim-Moser) aber und B. & H. heben den Eintritt durch erneuten Triller-Ansatz hervor.

Wilh. Altmann

# Quartet
## I

L. van Beethoven, Op. 59. № 1.
1770 - 1827

　　　E.E.1128　　　Ernst Eulenburg Ltd

**II**

Allegretto vivace e sempre scherzando. ♩.= 56

E.E.1128

E.E. 1128

E.E. 1128

E.E.1128

## III

Adagio molto e mesto. ♩=88 (♩=44)

cresc.
cresc.
cresc.
cresc.
f
f
p
pizz
p
arco
p
pizz.
arco
70
poco rit. -
pizz.
pp
a tempo
arco
pp
molto cantabile
pp

sempre stacc.

120

cresc.

cresc.

cresc.

cresc.

E.E.1128

E.E.1128

THEME RUSSE.

**IV**

Allegro. ♩ = 126

260

270